Printed and Published by D. C. Thomson & Co., Ltd.,
185 Fleet St., London, EC4A 2HS.
© D. C. Thomson & Co., Ltd., 1991.
ISBN 0-85116-520-6

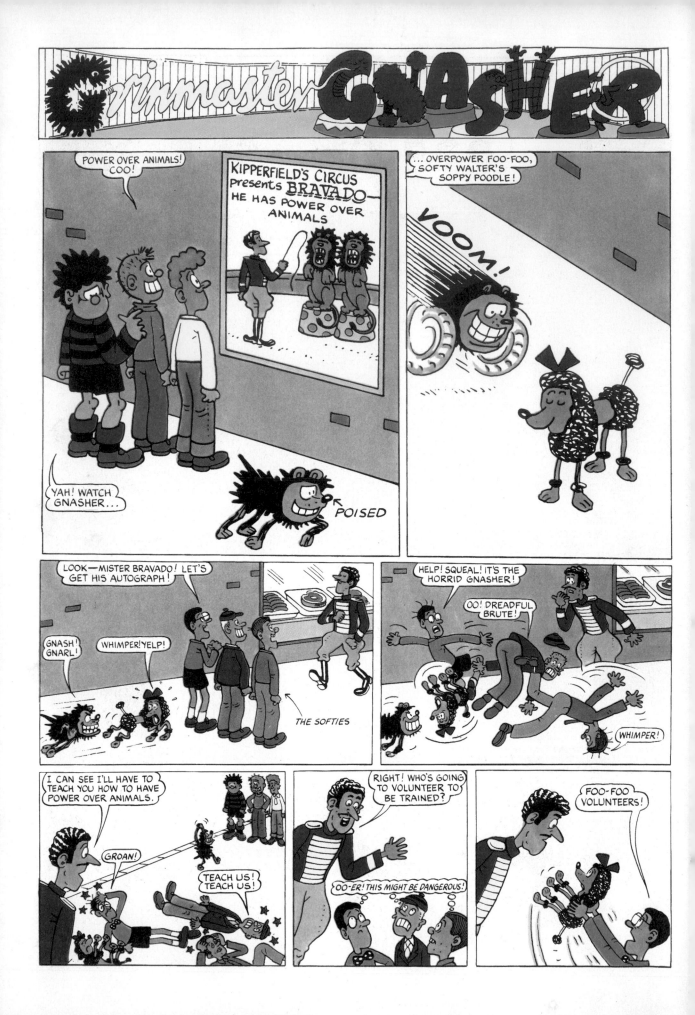

The NEW IMPROVED

FETCHES YOUR BEANO

NEWS

THEN DISPLAYS IT FOR YOU TO WATCH.

IT CAN PLAY YOUR FAVOURITE SONGS

ARIAS

PHUT! PHUT!

PROGRAMMED TO REJECT OPERA.

IF YOU WANT TO BE LIKE ME...
JOIN UP!
Mischief Enjoying, Naughty & Awful Children's Entertainment Society (M.E.N.A.C.E.S.) application form
Name (Only people with 'The' as a middle name need apply — Minnie The Minx, Attila The Hun etc.) ....
How far can you throw a softy? ....
How many people had to hold you down for your last haircut? ....
Have you ever done homework? (If yes, get lost.) ....
Which of these will deliver to your house without a police escort? Milkman, postman, S.A.S., Bert's very tough delivery service? ....
How long is your pocket money stopped for? ....
How many softies can you cram in an average litter bin? ....
Does your teacher wear a crash helmet? ....
Is your pet a dog? Crocodile? Pig? tiger? Very nasty hamster? ....
(If there are less than 10 spelling mistakes in your application form, you are expelled.)
HOW FRIGHTFUL! DEAR, SWEET CHUMMIES OF MINE GET THEIR CHANCE LATER IN THE BOOK—SO LOOK OUT YOUR LAVENDAR-COLOURED PENSY-WENSIES!

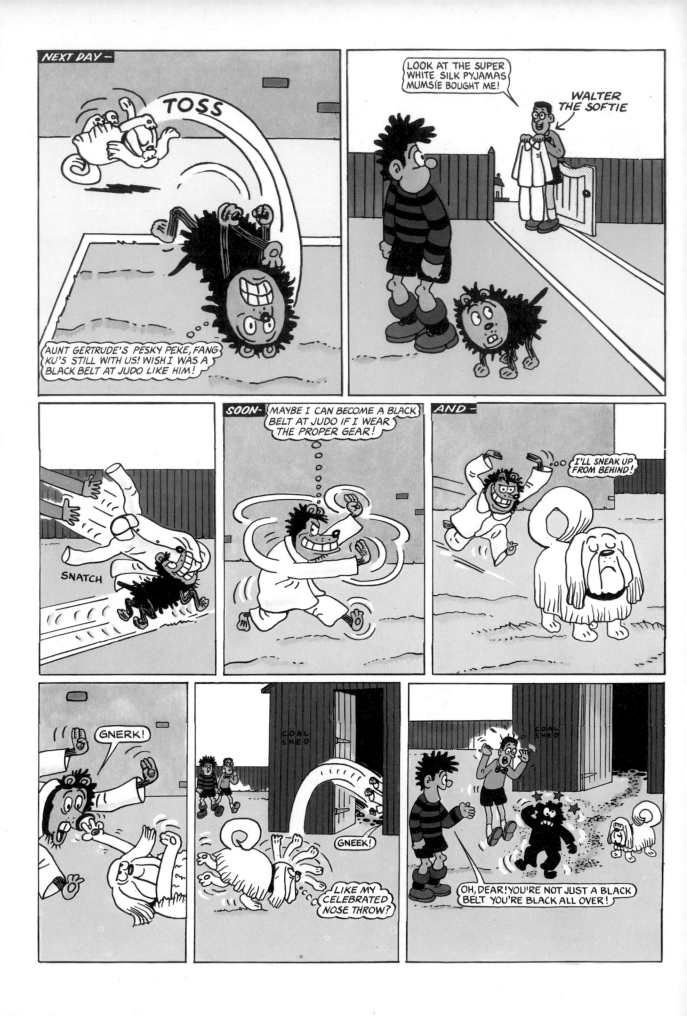

TODAY'S TELEVISION PROGRAMMES AT A GLANCE

MENACE TV

6.30 BREAKFAST TV
Anne Diamond reports on Dennis's attempts to smash the "Most Things Broken with a Catapult" record. (Watch your teeth, Anne!)

9.25 AFTER NINE
Dennis shows you lots of different ways to arrive late at school.

9.45 RAINBOW
Bungle, George and Zippy are joined by special guests Gnasher and Gnipper.

10.00 SEWING MASTERCLASS
Walter shows you how to patch and repair furry TV puppets destroyed by fierce black dogs.

10.30 NEWS AND WEATHER
Mum and Mrs O'Reilly next door discuss the state of Dad's bunion, the rising price of sprouts and how chilly it is for the time of year.

10.50 NEIGHBOURS AWAY
Menace TV's answer to Neighbours and Home and Away. In today's episode, the entire community leaves when Dennis drops a twenty megapong stink-bomb.

11.00 ANTIQUES ROADSHOW
Dennis's Granny and her cronies go out for a morning drive.

12.00 CLIMBWATCH
An update of Dennis's progress on his way up Walter's Apple tree.

12.30 MASH
Cookery tips as Dad gets the spuds ready for lunch.

1.00 FILM — HAMLET
Rasher stars in this remake of the Shakespearian classic.

3.00 RACING FROM MENACETOWN
Brough Scott brings you commentary on today's Hunters Chase when lots of angry gents with shotguns pursue Gnasher for scaring off all the pheasants and partridges in the area.

5.00 ALL SCREECHERS GREAT AND SMALL
Walter and his Soprano Choir give a recital of arias. (Warning — remove all crystal glasses from the room before tuning in.)

6.00 IT'S A KNOCK OUT
Jeremy Beadle makes the mistake of trying out one of his little tricks on Dennis. (Last in the present series).

7.00 THE BILL
Dad counts the cost of Dennis's visit to the glass factory.

8.00 CLOSEDOWN
Sorry, viewers — Dennis has been sent to bed without any supper.

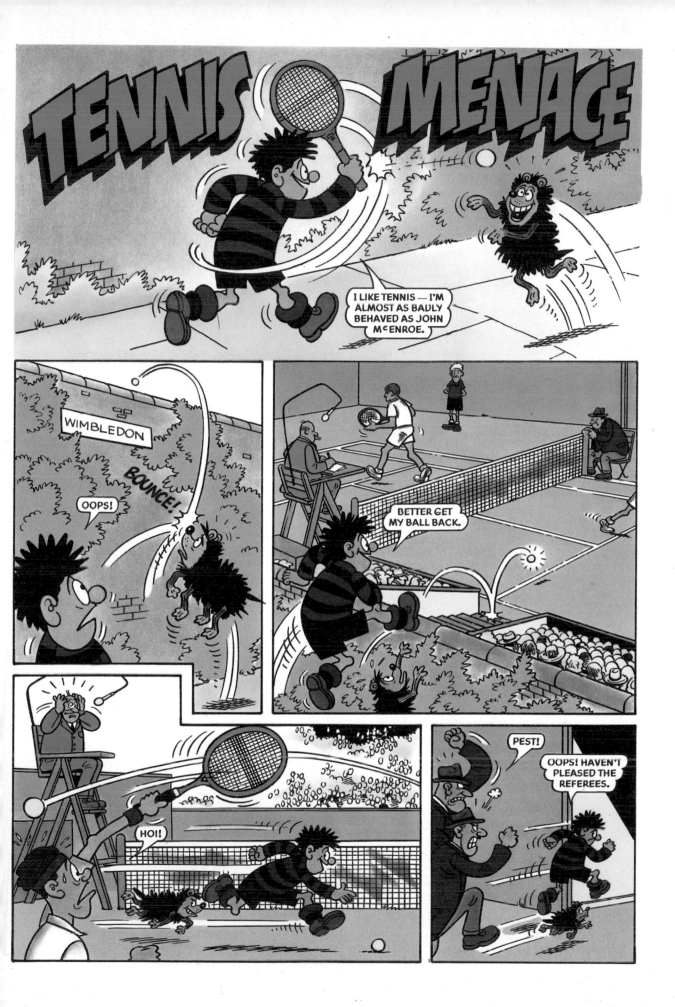

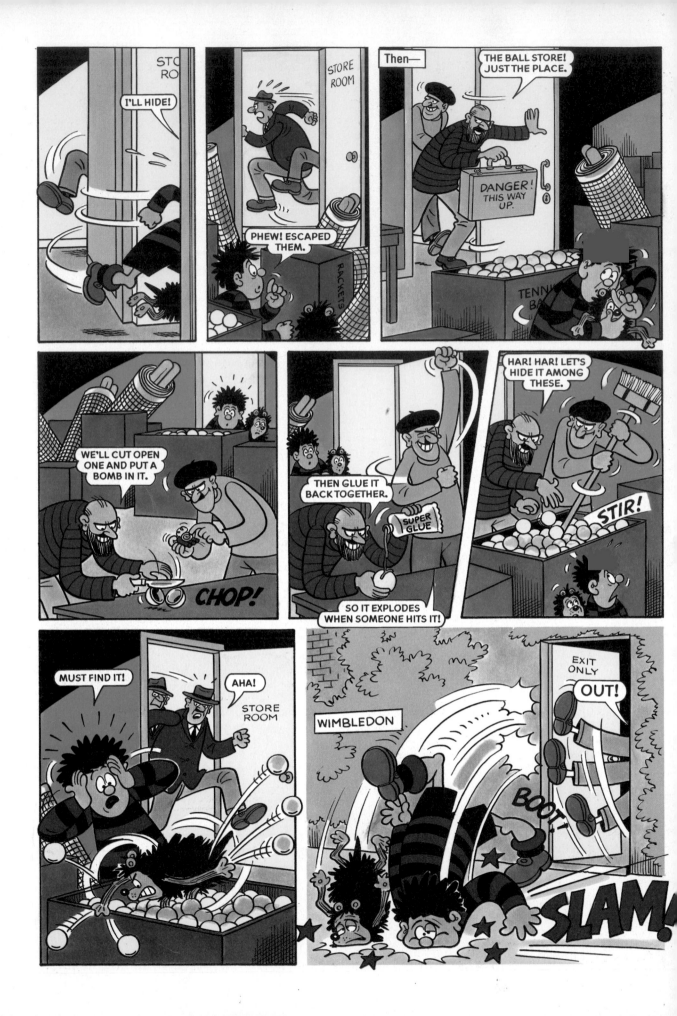

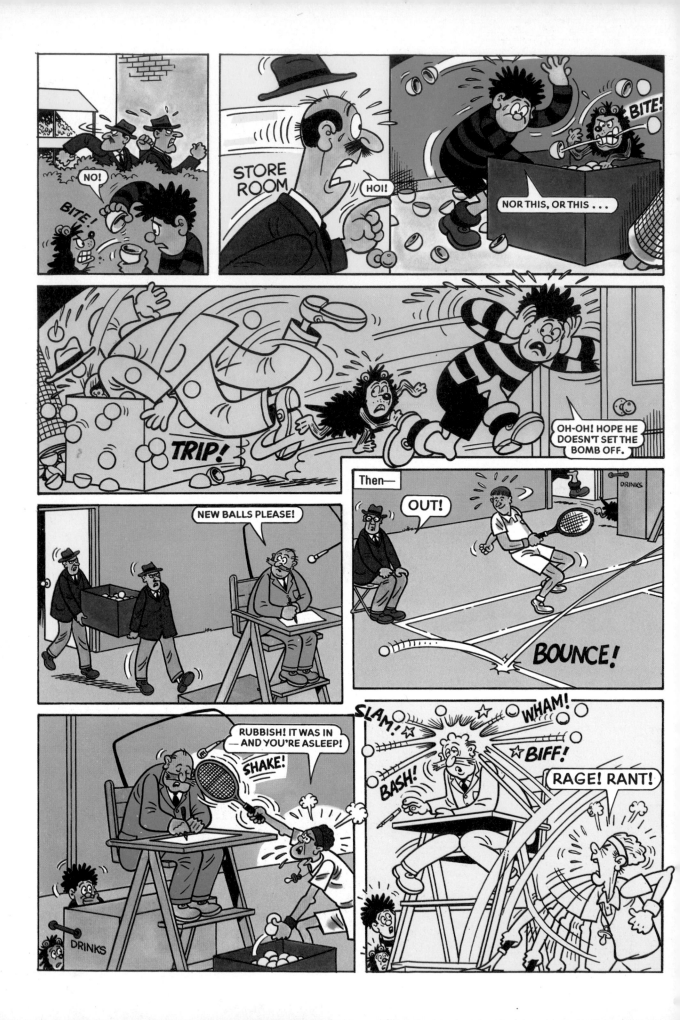

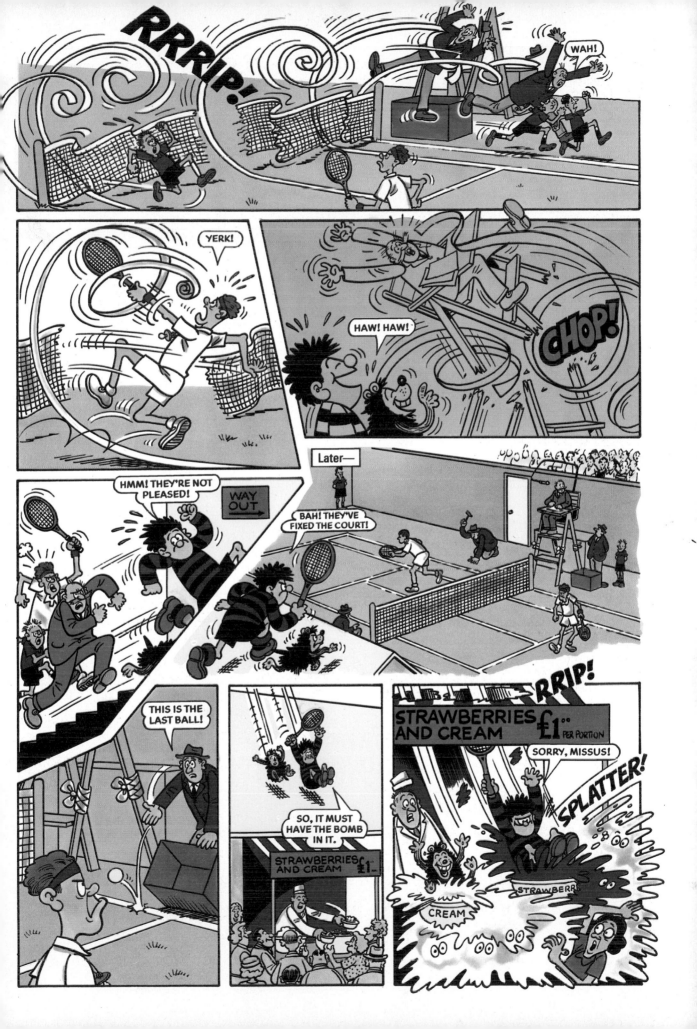

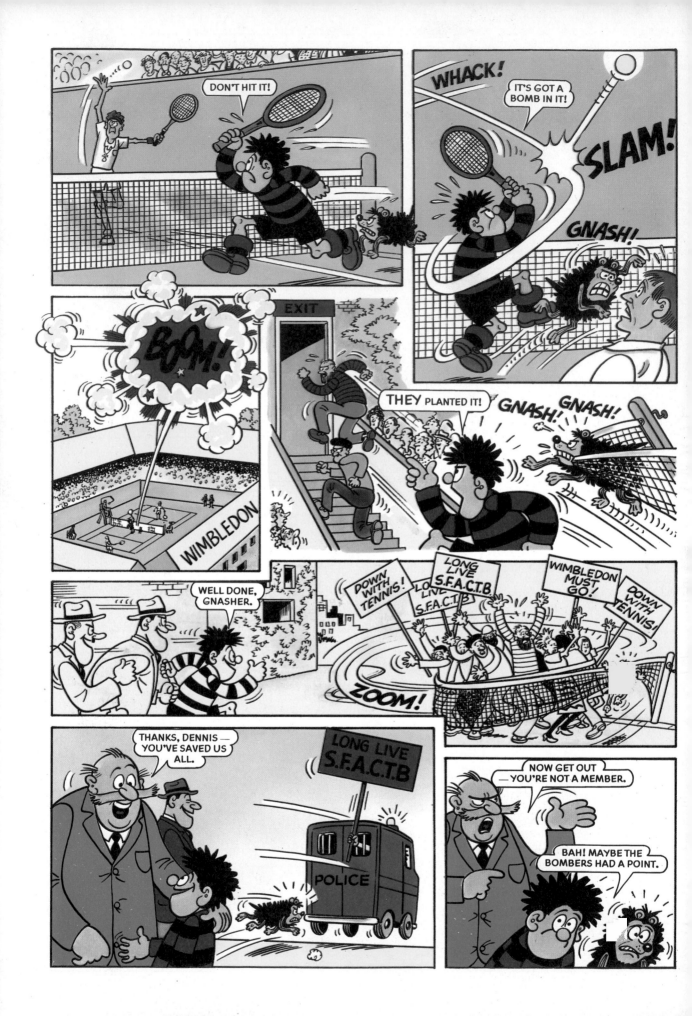

ON THE CREST OF A WAVE

FWOOSH! Down the hill sped one Menace on a skateboard. SWOOSH! Through a large muddy puddle swept the lad, giving an astonished Walter the Softy a surprise shower.

Walter was furious — he'd forgotten his scented shower gel and flowery cap.

"You absolute beast!" spluttered Walter. "What do you think you're playing at?"

"I'm off to Cornwall on holiday and guess what you can do there — GO SURFING! I thought I'd get in some practice for riding the waves by going through a few deep puddles on my skateboard.

"Going on holiday? I'll miss you," trilled Walter, his voice dripping with sarcasm (the rest of him was dripping with muddy water).

Soon Walter and his chummies were bidding the Menace family farewell as they sped off in their car packed to the roof with cases, buckets and spades and extremely smelly bones dug up from the garden (for Gnasher — not for Dad).

Five hours and 273 rounds of I-Spy later, Mum yawned, "I spy with my bloodshot eye, something beginning with 'W'."

"Wildebeest? Wireless? Wasp?

"Windscreen? Wellies? Warpaint?

"Wombat? Wallaby? Wahabee (one of a sect of Moslems founded in Central Arabia about 1760)?

"Womble? Walter? Weed?"

"No twelve times," said Mum. "Give in? The answer's WAVES — we're here!"

The car had barely stopped when a whooping, spiky-haired figure was hurtling down the beach tossing shorts, socks and red and black hooped jersey to the four winds, as he rocketed towards the sea yelling, "SURF'S UP!"

"DENNIS!" screamed Dad. "You don't have a surfboard!"

"But I DO have your suitcase,"

cackled Dennis, mounting a fifteen foot high breaker on Dad's best leather travelling bag.

It was at that very moment that Dennis discovered that surfing isn't quite as easy as it looks on TV.

With a gurgle, a splutter and three rather rude words, he toppled into the foaming briny and was soon glumly struggling from the water spurting salt water and seaweed.

his designer board and headed out to 'catch a wave'.

Dennis's faithful friend and sidekick, Gnasher, didn't like to see anyone laughing at his master (unless, of course, they were Beano readers laughing at his antics). So, at the same time as the surfing show off took to the waves, a small furry creature in a snorkel went underwater with a glint in his eye and his teeth.

The surf bum was good — you had to admit it. His tricks drew gasps of admiration from people on the beach and rasps of derision from Dennis.

Beneath the waves, a creature with teeth more menacing than Jaws or even Esther Rantzen was fast approaching.

Sadly his surfboard suitcase was not such a good swimmer and Dad's best suits, Mum's twinsets and undergarments and several gallons of suntan lotion were never seen again.

The sight of the soggy Menace looking like a drowned rat caused great merriment from a nearby bronzed youth sporting a natty "HARRY THE HUNK" tattoo on his golden chest.

"Haw-haw-haw", he guffawed, sounding very like one of the nearby beach donkeys. "The idea's to surf on *top* of the waves, not underneath them."

Watch an expert in action. At this, the less than modest young Adonis leapt on

"CHOMP!" Gnasher grabbed the fin of Harry's surfboard. SPLOSH! Off fell the surf rider into the water, where his nose was introduced to a rather large and ill-tempered lobster.

It was Dennis's turn to laugh like a drain as the yelping surf-bum abandoned his board and headed home so Mummy could kiss his nose better.

"Good old Gnasher!" laughed Dennis as his hound scrambled onto the board to wave to his beloved master.

Just then a wave bigger than a very big thing rose up behind Gnasher.

"GNASHEY!" yelled our toothy friend as he somersaulted and flipped the board on the wave to the applause and amazement of onlookers.

"What style!"

"What skill!"

"What a gnatural!"

Gnasher soon became the idol of the beach and earned doggy chocs galore giving surfing lessons for the rest of that holiday week.

"A great holiday, eh, Gnasher?" said Dennis happily as they headed home. But Gnasher wasn't in the car. Had he decided to stay to live the life of a beach dog?

Don't be silly! Here he is!

CORNWALL'S BUSTED

5 MLS TO HOME

IF YOU WANT TO BE LIKE ME...
JOIN UP!
Society Of Feeble Tender Youths (S.O.F.T.Y)
Application form for New Chumsies
Name (No rough ones, please) Cheryl McLaren
How many hankies did you use to mop up tears watching "Bambi"? none
What's your teddy's name? cuddles
And his favourite shade of pink? dark
How many curlers can you wear in your hairsy-wairsy without falling over? none
Do you have lace round the top of your socks? NO
Do you know any nasty rough boys? yes
Do you give your lovely teacher an apple every day or just every other day? no
What's your favourite ballet step? Dont
Can you eat crisps without muffs to protect your earsy-wearsys?
(Please send in a picture of yourself in an evening dress with this application).
PASSSSP!

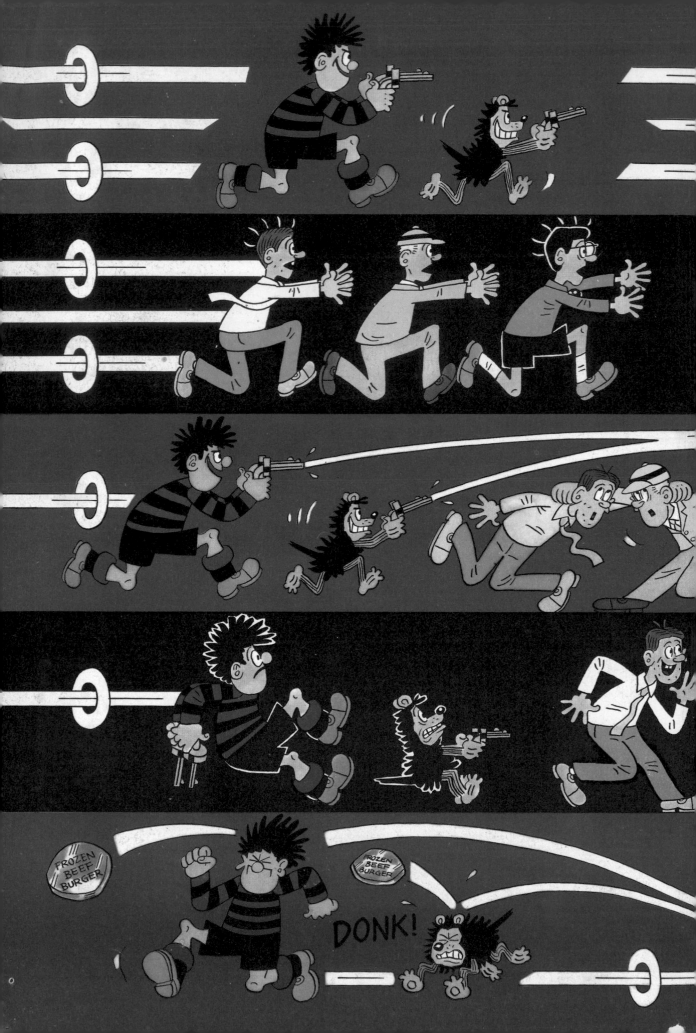

DONK!